Trust Me, JACK'S BEANSTALK STINKS!

The story of
JACK AND THE BEANSTALK
as told by
THE GIANT

by Eric Braun

www.raintreepublishers.co.uk
Visit our website to find out more information about Raintree books.

To order:
☎ Phone 0845 6044371
🖶 Fax +44 (0) 1865 312263
✉ Email myorders@raintreepublishers.co.uk

Customers from outside the UK please telephone +44 1865 312262

Raintree is an imprint of Capstone Global Library Limited, a company incorporated in England and Wales having its registered office at 7 Pilgrim Street, London, EC4V 6LB – Registered company number: 6695582

Text © Picture Window Books 2012
First published in the United Kingdom in 2012
The moral rights of the proprietor have been asserted.

We would like to thank Terry Flaherty, Professor of English at Minnesota State University, for his advice and expertise.

Editors: Jill Kalz and Vaarunika Dharmapala
Designer: Lori Bye
Art Director: Nathan Gassman
Production Specialist: Sarah Bennett
The illustrations in this book were created digitally.

ISBN 978 1 406 24312 3 (paperback)
16 15 14 13 12
10 9 8 7 6 5 4 3 2 1

British Library Cataloguing in Publication Data
A full catalogue record for this book is available from the British Library.

People think it's easy being a giant. You get to be rotten, grumpy, and loud. You're big and tough. You have stacks of treasure.

Best of all, **NOBODY** tells you how to behave.

Giant life is no picnic, though. It's hard to find shoes that fit. My knees hurt from the weight of my huge body. I'm always hungry. *Always.*

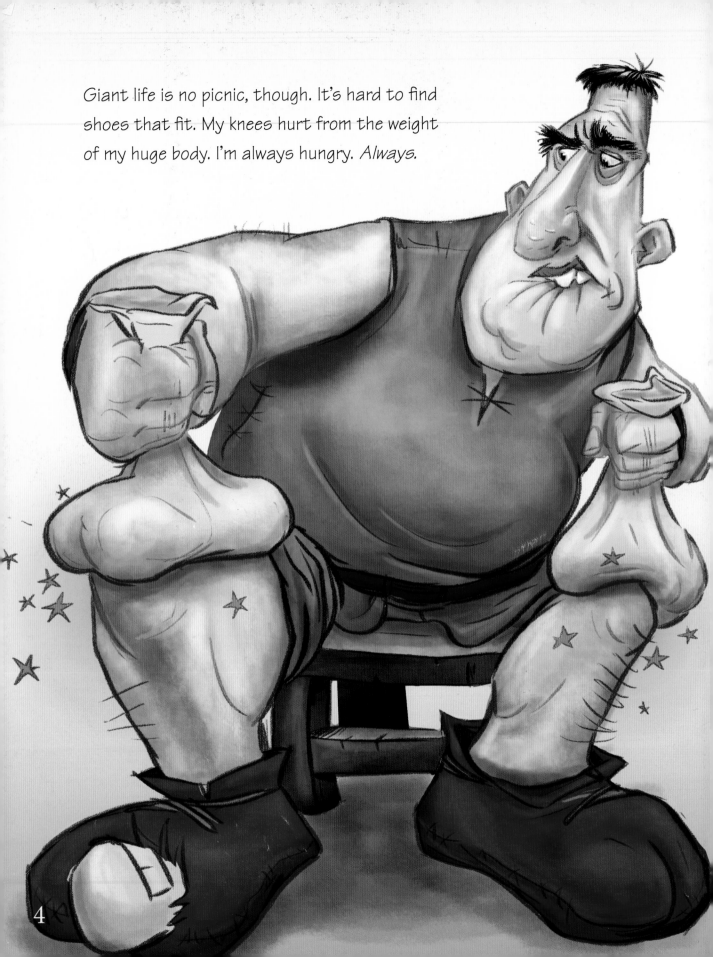

The worst thing of all is *humans*.

Humans are part of a balanced giant breakfast. When you're not eating them, though, they're a real pain. Sometimes they laugh at me behind my back. They call me "stinky" and "fatso". They ring my doorbell and run away. Ha ha ha, very funny!

This boy named Jack was extra bold. He came up through the clouds one day while I was out gathering a small breakfast. He tricked my wife into feeding him, then hid inside my house. I mean, come on. Would he hide inside a *human's* house? That's a crime!

Well, he didn't trick me. I could smell him.
(He smelled delicious.)

Perhaps you can still smell that Kiddie Kasserole from supper last night.

"FEE, FI, FO, FUM!"

I said. In Giant, this means something like,
"Go along home now. I promise I won't eat you."

He stayed in his hiding place, the little brat.

9

After breakfast, I took a nap as I always do.
Eating makes me tired. While I was sleeping,
Jack stole a bag of gold!

Humans: nutritious *and* sneaky.

Some time later, Jack came back. Once again, he tricked my wife into letting him inside.

When I came home from picking up a light breakfast, I could smell him. I knew who it was.

Perhaps you can still smell that Little Man Stew from supper last night.

"FEE, FI, FO, FUM!"

I yelled. This can also mean, "Give me back my gold, and we'll call it even. I definitely won't eat you."

He didn't come out.

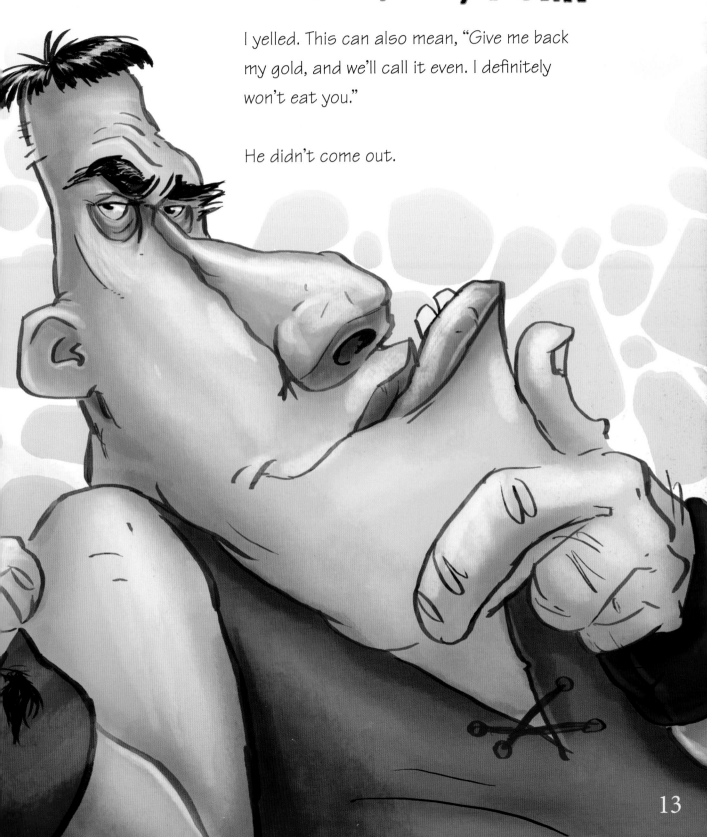

Just like the last time, I ate my meal and tried to forget about Jack. I relaxed with my goose, the one that lays golden eggs. Soon, I took a little snooze.

Of course that pesky boy couldn't let a chap rest. Do you know what he did?

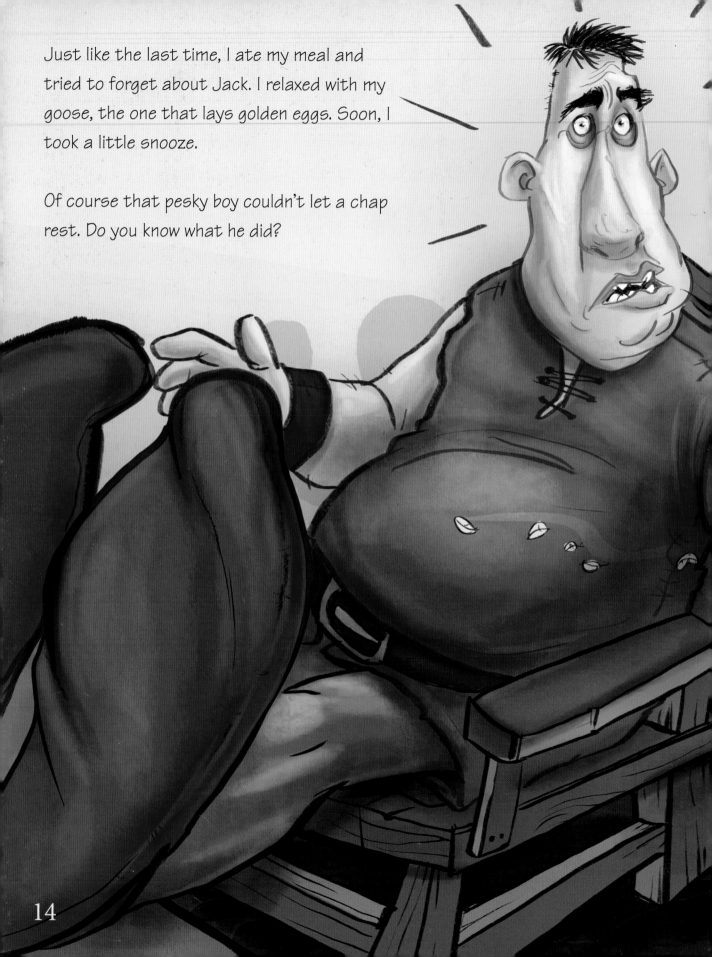

The next time Jack came round, I called out,

"FEE, FI, FO, FUM!"

This can sometimes mean, "Gosh, I'm really angry now!"

My wife and I searched everwhere, but we couldn't find him. I wanted to keep looking, but I got hungry. (Big surprise.)

After breakfast, I enjoyed some lovely music. My golden harp sang to me, and the sound was even sweeter than boy-berry tart. I rested my eyes a bit. I'd finally forgotten about Jack.

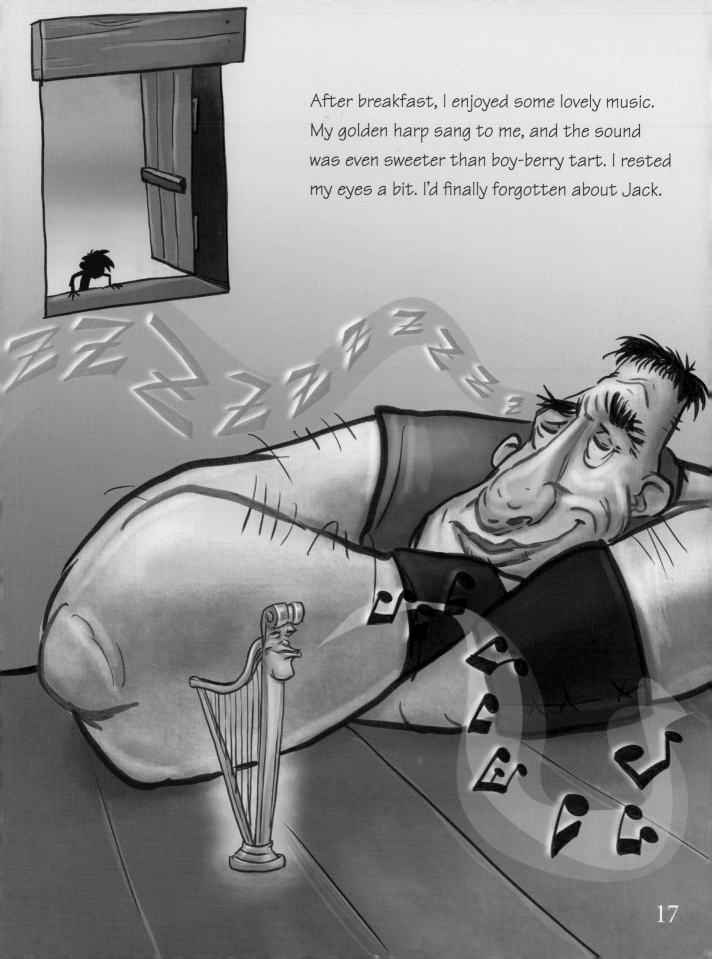

The next thing you know, my harp is calling, "Master! Master!" Jack was running off with it, and I thundered after them. I almost caught up to them, too, but they disappeared into the clouds.

Suddenly, there it was: a big beanstalk. Jack was climbing down it as quick as he could.

Well, I'm pretty intelligent. I know danger when I see it. I didn't want to go down there. No way! Then, my harp called out again.

So, down I went. Down, down …
That stalk was wobbly, but
I kept going.

The beanstalk shook once, twice, then toppled over. Jack had chopped it down with an axe! I fell and broke my crown. That's an old-fashioned way of saying I whacked my head really hard.

Even if you're a big, tough giant, that hurts.

My wife says I should forget about Jack. Sometimes, though, I still look down through the hole in the clouds.

Jack and his mother got rich selling golden eggs. They fattened up nicely. Then, Jack got married. My golden harp sang at the wedding. It was a lovely party.

I'll tell you one thing. Some day, when my crown feels better, I'm going to go down there to get my stuff back. Perhaps I'll grab lunch while I'm at it, too.